This Book
Belongs to:

378997

....

....

....

Consultant: Fiona Moss, RE Adviser at RE Today Services
Editor: Cathy Jones
Designer: Chris Fraser

First published in the UK in 2012 by
QED Publishing
A Quarto Group company
230 City Road
London EC1V 2TT

www.qed-publishing.co.uk

A catalogue record for this book is available
from the British Library.

ISBN 978 1 84835 892 8

Printed in China

David and Goliath

Written by
Katherine Sully

Illustrated by
Simona Sanfilippo

QED Publishing

One day, young David was
looking after the sheep when
he heard his father calling.

"Take this bread and cheese to your brothers," said his father. David's three older brothers were away fighting in King Saul's army.

Taking the bundle, David set off at once.

King Saul's army was camped on a hillside.
On the other hillside the Philistine army had gathered.

It was an amazing sight!

David searched among the lines of Saul's soldiers. He soon found his three brothers.

Just then, a giant soldier stepped forward
from the Philistine army.

He was so tall,
he towered over
everyone else!

He roared:
"I am Goliath, tall and mighty.
Who is brave enough to fight me?"

Not one of King Saul's soldiers replied.
They were all afraid!

The soldiers talked among themselves.

"The king will give a big prize to whoever kills the mighty giant Goliath," they said.

"What's going on?" young David asked his brothers.

"It's nothing to do with you," they said. "You're just a boy. Go home and look after the sheep."

But David did not go home.
He went to see King Saul in his tent.
"I will fight the giant," said David.

"I have killed a lion and a bear that tried to attack my sheep," said David. "I was not afraid because God looked after me."

"But you're ust a boy and ie is a mighty giant!" said the King.

King Saul gave David a
helmet, armour and a sword.

David put them on.
They were much too big!

He tried walking around
the tent.

"I can't wear
these," he said.
"I'm not used
to them."

Clink!
Clank!

He took them off again.

Instead, David took his sling and
his pouch and went down to the stream.

There he found
five smooth
stones and put
them in his pouch.

"My sling was all I needed to fight the lion and the bear," he thought. "God will look after me."

David went down to meet Goliath.
The giant towered over him. He roared:

"I am Goliath, tall and mighty.
Who is brave enough to fight me?"

"I am!" answered David.
"Will you fight me with that stick?"
sneered Goliath.

Goliath was angry!

Goliath lumbered towards David.

David grabbed a stone from his pouch and put it in his sling.

Goliath waved his sword in the air.

David let the stone fly through the air.

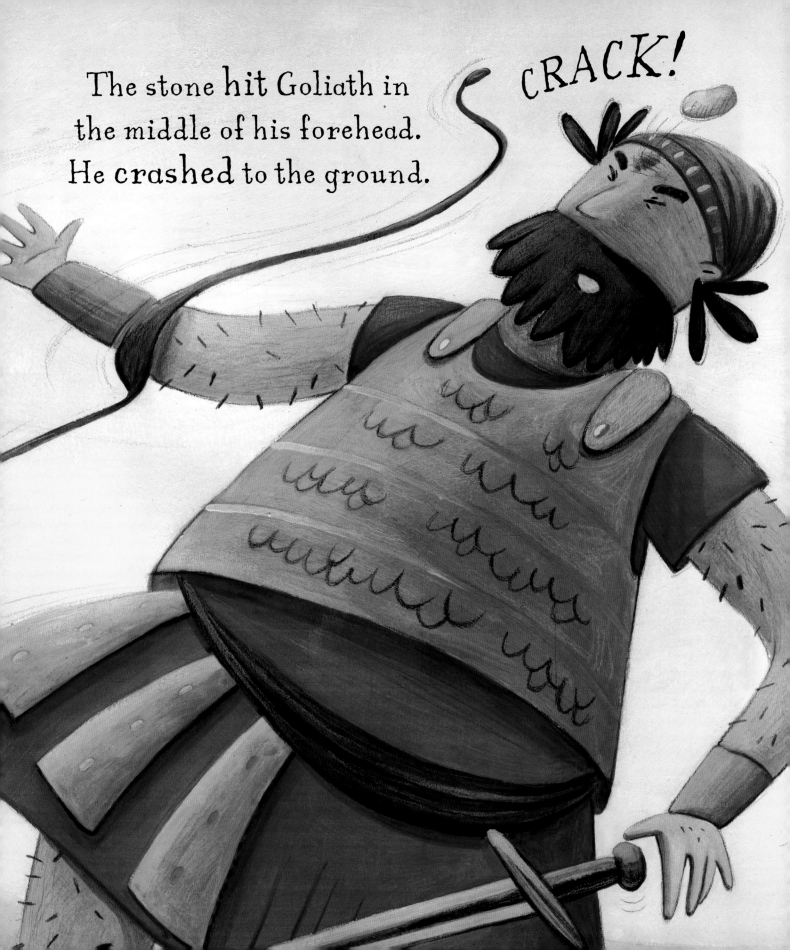

The stone hit Goliath in the middle of his forehead. He crashed to the ground.

CRACK!

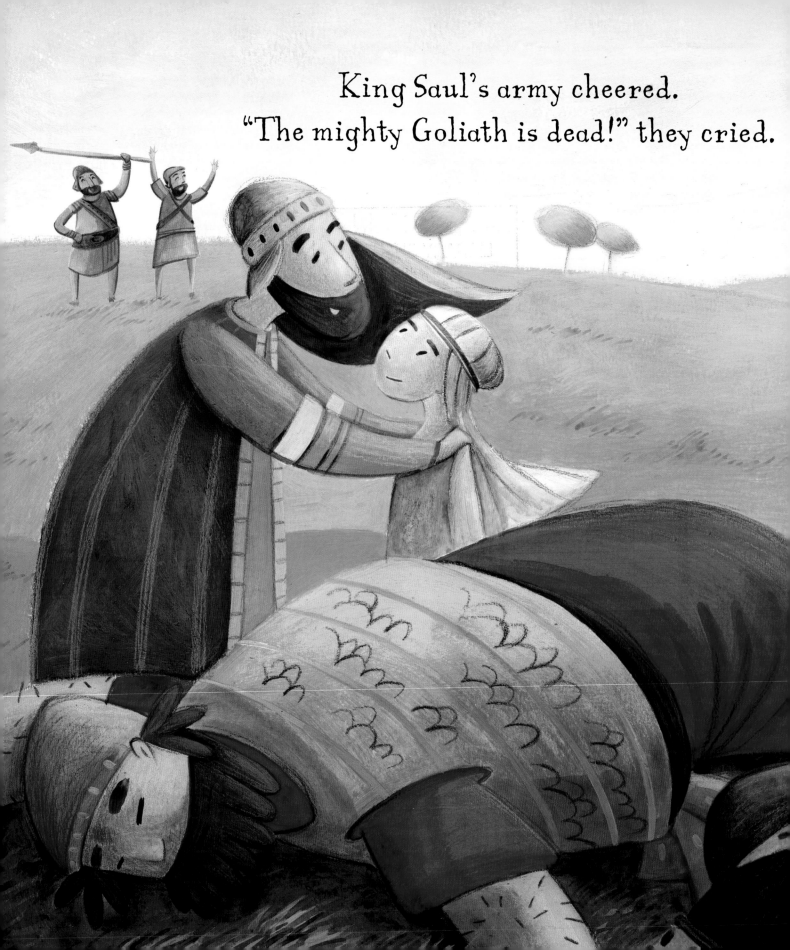

King Saul's army cheered.
"The mighty Goliath is dead!" they cried.

The Philistine army ran away,

chased by King Saul's soldiers.

Young David was a hero!

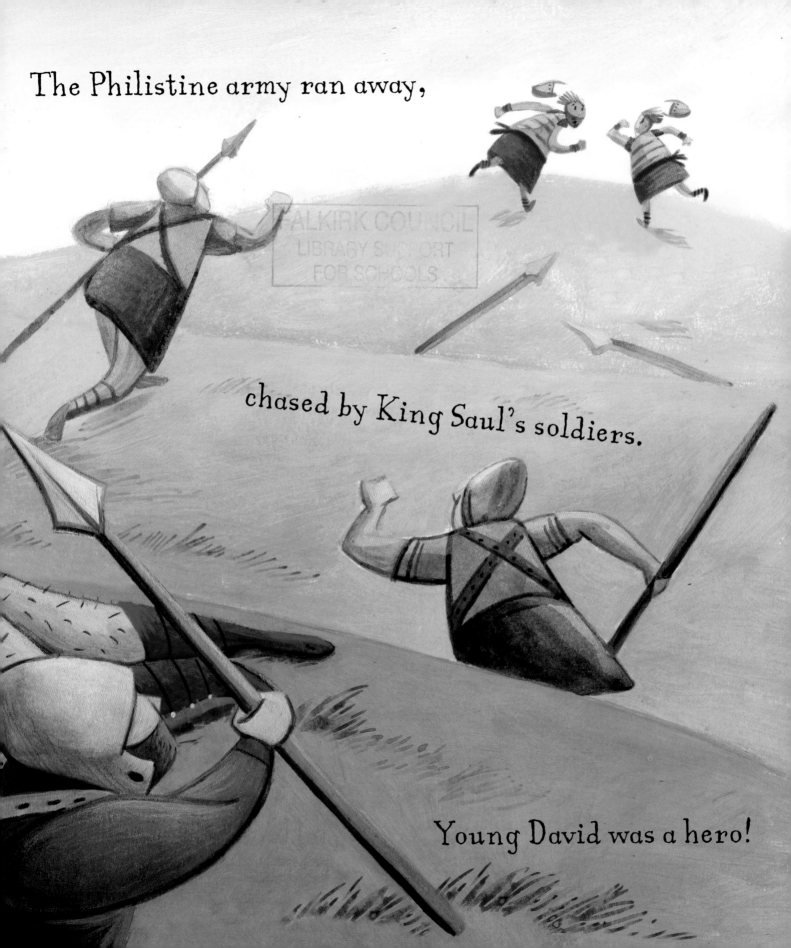

Next Steps

Look back through the book to find more to talk about and join in with.

* Make yourself big and tall. Make yourself small and short.
  Pretend you are throwing a shot from a sling. Pretend you have a sword.

* Join in with the rhyme. Pause to encourage joining in with,
  'I am Goliath, tall and mighty. Who is brave enough to fight me?'

* Goliath is 3 metres tall. Talk about how high that is, for example
  as high as a football post or an elephant.

* Name the colours of the tents. Look back through the book to
  spot the colours on other pages.

* Find shapes and sizes. Describe the armour that Goliath is
  wearing. Use words such as hard, stiff, shiny, metal, leather.

* Listen to the sounds. When you see the word on the page, point
  and make the sound – Clink! Clank! Crack!

Now that you've read the story... what do you remember?

* Who was David?
* Why did he go to find his brothers?
* Where did David find King Saul?
* What happened when David tried on the armour?
* How did David have the strength to fight Goliath?
* Why did Goliath crash to the ground?

What does the story tell us?
We can face big problems if God is on our side.